Working Papers

Introduction to FINANCIAL ACCOUNTING

Dudley W. Curry
Ph.D., C.P.A., Southern Methodist University

Working Papers

Introduction to FINANCIAL ACCOUNTING

Charles T. Horngren

PRENTICE-HALL, INC., *Englewood Cliffs, New Jersey 07632*

Printed in the United States of America

10 9 8 7 6 5 4 3 2 1

0-13-483727-4

Prentice-Hall International, Inc., *London*
Prentice-Hall of Australia Pty. Limited, *Sydney*
Prentice-Hall of Canada, Ltd., *Toronto*
Prentice-Hall of India Private Limited, *New Delhi*
Prentice-Hall of Japan, Inc., *Tokyo*
Prentice-Hall of Southeast Asia Pte. Ltd., *Singapore*
Whitehall Books Limited, *Wellington, New Zealand*

TO THE STUDENT

This is a set of working papers for solving most of the problem assignments in *Introduction to Financial Accounting* by Charles T. Horngren. These working papers can save you time because they contain much of the information required by the problems. No forms are provided for the questions or other assignments that can be answered on any kind of paper.

NAME ____________________

DATE __________ CLASS SECTION __________

1-2
Balance Sheet Effects

(Sample answers are given for 1a and 1b)

	Assets	= Liabilities	+ Owners' Equity
1. (a)	Telephone Plant		
	+ 50 million		
	Other Assets (cash)		
	– 50 million		
(b)	Telephone plant	Long-term Debt	
	+ 50 million	+ 40 million	
	Other Assets (cash)		
	– 10 million		
2.			
3.			
4.			

	Assets	= Liabilities	+ Owners' Equity
5. (a)			
(b)			
6.			
7.			
8.			

NAME ____________________

DATE ________ CLASS SECTION ________

SPAN CLEANERS
Analysis of April Transactions
(in thousands of dollars)

	ASSETS			=	EQUITIES		
	Cash	Accounts Receivable	Equipment and Furniture	=	Note Payable	Accounts Payable	Owners' Equity
a.				=			
b.				=			
c.				=			
d.				=			
e.				=			
f.				=			
g.				=			
h.				=			
i.				=			
Tot.				=			

SPAN CLEANERS

Balance Sheet

April 30, 19x1

Assets		Equities	
		Liabilities:	

NAME ____________________

DATE ________ CLASS SECTION ________

Prepare Balance Sheet

CONE CORPORATION

Balance Sheet

August 31, 19x1

Assets		Equities	
		Liabilities:	

NAME ______________________________

DATE __________ CLASS SECTION __________

	ASSETS				=	EQUITIES		
	Cash	Receivables	Inventory	Equipment	=	Accounts Payable	Note Payable	Owners' Equity
1.					=			
2.					=			
3.					=			
4.					=			
5.					=			
6.					=			
7.					=			
8.					=			
9.					=			
10.					=			
11.					=			
12.					=			
13.					=			
14.					=			
15.					=			
Tot.					=			

APEX DISTRIBUTORS

Balance Sheet

March 31, 19x1

Assets		Equities	
		Liabilities:	

NAME ____________________

DATE ________ CLASS SECTION ________

MARY DAIMEN, REALTOR

Balance Sheet

November 30, 19x1

Assets		Equities	
		Liabilities:	

MARY DAIMEN, PERSONAL

Balance Sheet

November 30, 19x1

Assets		Equities	
		Liabilities:	

NAME ______________________________

DATE __________ CLASS SECTION __________

Analysis of Business Transactions

	Assets						=	Liabilities			Owner's Equity
	Cash	Note Receivable	Rental Deposit	Dental Supplies	Dental Equipt.	Office Furn.	=	Note Payable	Account Payable	Payable to Gibson	Gibson Capital
1							=				
2							=				
3							=				
4							=				
5							=				
6							=				
7							=				
8							=				
9							=				
10							=				
11							=				
Tot.							=				

Analysis of Personal Transactions

	Assets							=	Liabilities		Owner's Equity
	Cash	Receivable, Dental Office	Receivable, Brother	Investment in Stocks	Investment, Dent. Prac.	Personal Residence	Home Furniture	=	Accounts Payable	Mortgage Payable	Gibson Capital
1								=			
2								=			
3								=			
4								=			
5								=			
6								=			
7								=			
8								=			
9								=			
10								=			
11								=			
Tot.								=			

J. GIBSON, DENTIST

Balance Sheet
December 31, 19x1

Assets		Equities	
		Liabilities:	

J. GIBSON, PERSONAL

Balance Sheet
December 31, 19x1

Assets		Equities	
		Liabilities:	

NAME ______________________

DATE ________ CLASS SECTION ________

	Assets	= Liabilities	+ Owners' Equity
1.			
2.			
3.			
4.			
5.			

1-20 (Continued)

	Assets	= Liabilities	+ Owners' Equity
6.			
7.			
8.			
9.			
10.			

NAME ____________________

DATE ________ CLASS SECTION ________

Balance Sheet Effects

	Assets	= Liabilities	+ Owners' Equity
1.			
2.			
3.			

NAME ____________________

DATE ________ CLASS SECTION ________

Prepare Balance Sheet

CROWN ZELLERBACH CORPORATION

Balance Sheet

December 31, 1978

(in thousands of dollars)

Assets	Equities
	Liabilities:

NAME ________________________________

DATE ________ CLASS SECTION ________

	Assets			=	Equities	
Name of Entity	Cash	Receivables & Prepayments	Trucks & Other Assets	=	Various Payables	Owners' Equity
1. Safeway Stores				=		
Herbert Simon				=		
2. Sears Roebuck				=		
Kenneth Arrow				=		
3. Amer. Express				=		
Michael Harrison				=		
4. Bank of Amer.				=		
David Kreps				=		
5. United Airlines				=		
Robert Wilson				=		
6. Fidelity Savings				=		
Evan Porteus				=		
8. Time				=		
Charles Bonini				=		
9. Postal Service				=		
Gen. Serv. Admin.				=		
10. U.S. Treasury				=		
Lockheed Corp.				=		

NAME ______________________________

DATE __________ CLASS SECTION __________

(amounts in thousands)

	Assets					=	Equities			
							Liabilities		Stockholders' Equity	
	Cash	Accounts Receivable	Mdse. Inventory	Prepaid Rent	Equipment & Furniture	=	Note Payable	Accounts Payable	Paid-in Capital	Retained Income
1						=				
2						=				
3						=				
4a						=				
4b						=				
5						=				
6						=				
7						=				
8						=				
9						=				
10						=				
11						=				
12						=				
Bal.						=				

DORIAN COMPANY
Balance Sheet
March 31, 19x1

Assets	Equities
	Liabilities:

DORIAN COMPANY
Income Statement
For the Month Ended March 31, 19x1

Analysis of performance:

NAME ______________________________

DATE ________ CLASS SECTION ________

DORIAN COMPANY
Income Statement
(Cash Basis)

For the Month Ended March 31, 19X1

Comparison with accrual basis income statement:

NAME ______________________

DATE __________ CLASS SECTION __________

(amounts in thousands)

	Assets						=	Equities			
								Liabilities		Stockholders' Equity	
	Cash	Accounts Receivable	Mdse. Inventory	Prepaid Rent	Prepaid Insurance	Equipment	=	Note Payable	Accounts Payable	Paid-in Capital	Retained Income
1							=				
2							=				
3							=				
4							=				
5							=				
6							=				
7							=				
8							=				
9							=				
10							=				
11							=				
12							=				
13							=				
Bal.							=				

Comments on Transactions 8-11:

ROWLEY COMPANY
Income Statement
For the Month Ended June 30, 19X1

ROWLEY COMPANY
Balance Sheet
June 30, 19X1

Assets		Equities	
		Liabilities:	

NAME ________________

DATE ________ CLASS SECTION ________

ROWLEY COMPANY
Income Statement
For the Month Ended June 30, 19X1

Discussion:

NAME ______________________________

DATE ________ CLASS SECTION ________

(amounts in thousands)

	Assets					=	Equities		
1. Two Phases	**Cash**	**Prepaid Rent**	**Supplies**	**Unexpired Advertising**	**Unexpired Training**	=	**Liab.**	**Pd.-in Cap.**	**Retained Income**
(a) 1						=			
(a) 2						=			
(b) 1						=			
(b) 2						=			
(c) 1						=			
(c) 2						=			
(d) 1						=			
(d) 2						=			
Totals						=			
2. Shortcut									
(a)						=			
(b)						=			
(c)						=			
(d)						=			
Totals						=			

NAME ______________________

DATE __________ CLASS SECTION __________

2. Assets		Equities	

3. Assets		Equities	

Comments:

4. Assets		Equities	

Comments:

5. Assets		Equities	

Comments:

NAME ____________________

DATE ________ CLASS SECTION ________

Transactions	ASSETS					=	EQUITIES			
							Liabilities		Stockholders' Equity	
	Cash	Accounts Receivable	Inventory	Prepaid Rent	Store Equipment	=	Note Payable	Accounts Payable	Paid-in Capital	Retained Income
Balances, Jan. 12, 19X2	342,700	300	159,200	- 0 -	14,000	=	100,000	16,200	400,000	- 0 -
10 a. Sales						=				
10 b. Cost of inventory sold						=				
11. Paid rent in advance						=				
12. Recognized expired rent						=				
13. Recognized depreciation						=				
EX Paid cash dividends						=				
Balances, Jan. 31, 19X2						=				

BIWHEELS COMPANY
Income Statement
For the Month Ended January 31, 19X2

BIWHEELS COMPANY
Statement of Retained Income
For the Month Ended January 31, 19X2

BIWHEELS COMPANY
Balance Sheet
January 31, 19X2

Assets		Equities	
		Liabilities:	

NAME ______________________________

DATE __________ CLASS SECTION __________

Prepare Financial Statements

COMPLETION CORPORATION
Income Statement
For the Year Ended December 31, 19X2

COMPLETION CORPORATION
Statement of Retained Income
For the Year Ended December 31, 19X2

COMPLETION CORPORATION
Balance Sheet
December 31, 19X2

Assets

Equities

Liabilities:

NAME ______________________________

DATE __________ CLASS SECTION __________

(show amounts in thousands)

	Assets					=	Equities		
Transactions	**Cash**	**Accounts Receivable**	**Inventory**	**Prepaid Rent**	**Equipment**	=	**Accounts Payable**	**Paid-in Capital**	**Retained Income**
Bal., Dec. 31, 19X1	100	400	800	40	90	=	700	160	570
a. Acquired inventory						=			
b. Sales						=			
c. Cost of inventory sold						=			
d1. Old lease expired						=			
d2. Lease renewal paid						=			
d3. New lease expired						=			
e. Depreciation expense						=			
f. Collected receivables						=			
g. Paid wages						=			
h. Paid misc. expenses						=			
i. Paid payables						=			
j. Dividends						=			
Bal., Dec. 31, 19X2						=			

HUTTON LIGHTING COMPANY
Income Statement
For the Year Ended December 31, 19X2

(in thousands)

HUTTON LIGHTING COMPANY
Statement of Retained Income
For the Year Ended December 31, 19X2

(in thousands)

HUTTON LIGHTING COMPANY
Statement of Income and Retained Income
For the Year Ended December 31, 19X2

(in thousands)

2-33 (Continued)

HUTTON LIGHTING COMPANY
Balance Sheet
December 31, 19x2
(in thousands)

Assets		Equities	
		Liabilities:	

NAME ______________________

DATE ________ CLASS SECTION ________

HIGGINS COMPANY

Income Statement

For the Year Ended December 31, 19X2

(in thousands)

Comments:

NAME ______________________

DATE ________ CLASS SECTION ________

THE BOEING COMPANY
Statement of Net Earnings and Retained Earnings
For the Year Ended December 31, 1978

(in millions)

NAME ______________________________

DATE ________ CLASS SECTION ________

1.

McDONALD'S CORPORATION
Income Statement
For the Year Ended December 31, 1978
(in thousands)

McDONALD'S CORPORATION
Statement of Retained Income
For the Year Ended December 31, 1978
(in thousands)

2. Comments:

NAME ______________________________

DATE __________ CLASS SECTION __________

(in thousands)	LEVITZ					UNITED AIRLINES			
	ASSETS		=	L	SE	A	=	L	SE
		Prepaid			Travel			Def. Sales	Sales
Transaction	Cash	Travel			Expense	Cash		Revenue	Revenue
1. December			=				=		
payment									
2. February			=				=		
travel									

NAME ____________________

DATE ________ CLASS SECTION ________

3-21 and 3-22

Interest Analysis

3-21	SEARS, LENDER						RIEGAL, BORROWER				
	Assets			=	L	SE	A	=	Liabilities		SE
Date	Cash	Note Receivable	Interest Receivable			Interest Revenue	Cash		Note Payable	Interest Payable	Interest Expense
3-22											

NAME ________________________________

DATE __________ CLASS SECTION __________

	ASSETS					=	LIABILITIES				SE	
	Cash	Accts. Rec.	Inv.	Prep. Rent	Fixt. & Equip.	=	Accts. Pay.	Notes Pay.	Accrued Wages	Accrued Int.	Pd. In Cap.	Retained Income
1						=						
2						=						
3a						=						
3b						=						
4a						=						
4b						=						
5a						=						
5b	*					=						
6a						=						
6b						=						
7						=						
8						=						
9						=						
10						=						
11						=						
Bal.						=						

*Show computations on reverse side.

SARTORIAL CHOICE, INC.
Income Statement
For the Month Ended April 30, 19X1

SARTORIAL CHOICE, INC.
Statement of Retained Income
For the Month Ended April 30, 19X1

SARTORIAL CHOICE, INC.
Balance Sheet
April 30, 19X1

Assets		Equities	
		Liabilities:	

Computations for 5b:

Advice to owners:

NAME ______________________

DATE ________ CLASS SECTION ________

CONNECTION DISTRIBUTORS, INC.
Income Statement
For the Year Ended December 31, 19X3

CONNECTION DISTRIBUTORS, INC.
Statement of Retained Income
For the Year Ended December 31, 19X3

3-28 (Continued)

CONNECTION DISTRIBUTORS, INC.
Balance Sheet
December 31, 19x3

Assets		Equities	
Ratios:			

NAME ____________________

DATE __________ CLASS SECTION __________

DR. CHRISTINA FARAGHER, DENTIST
Income Statement
For the Year Ended December 31, 19X7

	Cash Basis	Accrual Basis
Fee Revenue		
Expenses:		

Comments:

NAME ____________________

DATE __________ CLASS SECTION __________

	ASSETS		=	L	SE
Description of Transaction or Event	Cash	Unexpired Services	=	Accrued Wages	Wages Expense
1.			=		
			=		
			=		
			=		
Total effects			=		
2.			=		
			=		
Total effects			=		

NAME ______________________________

DATE __________ CLASS SECTION __________

Description of Transaction or Event	ASSETS			=	L	SE	
	Cash	Soap on Hand	Unexpd. Adv.	=		Soap Expense	Adv. Expense
1.							
2.							

Comments: ______________________________

NAME ______________________

DATE __________ CLASS SECTION __________

PORTLAND GENERAL ELECTRIC COMPANY

Income Statement

For the Year Ended December 31, 1978

PORTLAND GENERAL ELECTRIC COMPANY

Statement of Retained Earnings

For the Year Ended December 31, 1978

NAME ______________________________

DATE ________ CLASS SECTION ________

ANHEUSER-BUSCH, INC.
Statement of Income and Retained Earnings
For the Year Ended December 31, 1978
(in thousands)

Ratios and Percentages:

NAME ______________________________

DATE ________ CLASS SECTION ________

SAFEWAY STORES

Statement of Income and Retained Earnings

For the Year Ended December 31, 1978

(in thousands)

Ratios and Percentages:

NAME ______________________________

DATE __________ CLASS SECTION __________

GENERAL LEDGER

Cash

JOURNAL ENTRIES	DR.	CR.

		JOURNAL ENTRIES	DR.	CR.

HARTMAN SPORTING GOODS
Trial Balance
February 28, 19X2

	DR.	CR.

HARTMAN SPORTING GOODS
Income Statement
For the Month Ended February 28, 19X2

HARTMAN SPORTING GOODS
Statement of Retained Income
For the Month Ended February 28, 19X2

HARTMAN SPORTING GOODS
Balance Sheet
February 28, 19X2

Assets

Current assets:

Equities

Current liabilities:

NAME ____________________

DATE ________ CLASS SECTION ________

		JOURNAL ENTRIES	DR.	CR.

4-4 (Continued)

		JOURNAL ENTRIES		DR.	CR.

General Ledger

Cash

JANE PEREZ, REALTOR
Trial Balance
March 31, 19X1

	DR.	CR.

NAME ____________________

DATE ________ CLASS SECTION ________

		JOURNAL ENTRIES		DR.	CR.

JOURNAL ENTRIES	DR.	CR.

GENERAL LEDGER

Cash

NAME ____________________

DATE ________ CLASS SECTION ________

JOURNAL ENTRIES	DR.	CR.

		JOURNAL ENTRIES		DR.	CR.

NAME ____________________

DATE __________ CLASS SECTION __________

GENERAL LEDGER

Cash 10

Entry No.	JOURNAL ENTRIES	Post Ref.	DR.	CR.

GOODHUE STATIONERY SUPPLIES
Trial Balance
December 31, 19x5
(in thousands)

Acct. No.	Account Title	DR.	CR.

NAME ____________________

DATE ________ CLASS SECTION ________

Date		JOURNAL ENTRIES	Post Ref.	DR.	CR.

DRYDEN LAUNDRY AND CLEANING COMPANY
Trial Balance
January 3, 19x3

Acct. No.	Account Title	DR.	CR.

4-21 (Continued)

Cash

Account No.

Date	Explanation	Journ. Ref.	Amount	Date	Explanation	Journ. Ref.	Amount

Accounts Receivable

No.

Equipment

No.

Accounts Payable

No.

Note Payable

No.

Paid-in Capital

No.

Sales

No.

Supplies Expense

No.

Wages Expense

No.

NAME ________________

DATE ________ CLASS SECTION ________

GAMBREL AUTO PARTS STORE
Trial Balance
December 31, 19X7

	DR.	CR.

NAME ______________________________

DATE __________ CLASS SECTION __________

Cash

Date		JOURNAL ENTRIES	Post Ref.	DR.	CR.

Date		JOURNAL ENTRIES	DR.	CR.

TELEVISION REPAIR SERVICE
Trial Balance
January 31, 19X2

	DR.	CR.

NAME ____________________

DATE ________ CLASS SECTION ________

		JOURNAL ENTRIES	DR.	CR.

NAME ______________________________

DATE ________ CLASS SECTION ________

		JOURNAL ENTRIES	DR.	CR.

Cash

Dues Receivable

Deferred Dues Revenue

Dues Revenue – 19X1

Dues Revenue – 19X2

NAME ______________________________

DATE __________ CLASS SECTION __________

		JOURNAL ENTRIES	DR.	CR.

Cash

Subscriptions Receivable

Deferred Subscription Revenue

Subscription Revenue Earned

NAME ______________________________

DATE __________ CLASS SECTION __________

		JOURNAL ENTRIES	DR.	CR.

Cash

Rent Receivable

Deferred Rental Revenue

Rent Revenue Earned

NAME ______________________

DATE __________ CLASS SECTION __________

		JOURNAL ENTRIES	DR.	CR.

Accounts Receivable

Deferred Income

Income from Service Contracts

NAME ______________________________

DATE ________ CLASS SECTION ________

JOURNAL ENTRIES (in thousands)	DR.	CR.

Cash or Accounts Receivable

Operating Revenues

Advance Billing and Customers' Deposits

NAME ____________________

DATE ________ CLASS SECTION ________

		1. JOURNAL ENTRIES (in thousands)	DR.	CR.
		2. Account titles and effects:		

NAME ____________________

DATE ________ CLASS SECTION ________

Entry		Accounts and Explanation	Post Ref.	(in thousands) DR.	CR.

Entry		Accounts and Explanation	Post Ref.	(in thousands) DR.	CR.

(in thousands)

Cash

SERBEIN COMPANY Trial Balances Dec. 31, 19x2 (in thousands)

Account Title	Adjusted		Post-Closing	
	DR.	Cr.	DR.	CR.

NAME ______________________

DATE ________ CLASS SECTION ________

Entry		Accounts and Explanation	Post Ref.	(in thousands) DR.	CR.

Entry		Accounts and Explanations	Post Ref.	(in thousands) DR.	CR.

Entry	Accounts and Explanation	Post Ref.	(in thousands) DR.	CR.

(in thousands)

Cash 10

WRIZ LUMBER
Trial Balance
December 31, 19X2

(in thousands)	DR.	CR.

WRIZ LUMBER
Income Statement
For the Year Ended December 31, 19X2
(in thousands)

WRIZ LUMBER
Statement of Retained Income
For the Year Ended December 31, 19X2
(in thousands)

WRIZ LUMBER
Balance Sheets
(in thousands)

	December 31	
Assets	19X2	19X1
Current assets:		
Equities		
Current liabilities:		

Assignment 5-4

Current Ratio

Current debt to stockholders' equity:

Total debt to stockholders' equity:

Net income on sales:

Net income on stockholders' equity:

Collection period (days):

Inventory turnover:

Gross profit to sales:

Comments:

NAME ____________________

DATE ________ CLASS SECTION ________

Entry	Accounts and Explanation	Post Ref.	DR. (in thousands)	CR. (in thousands)

WONG ENGINEERING CONSULTANTS, INC.
Adjusted Trial Balance
June 30, 19X5

(in thousands)	DR.	CR.

(in thousands)

Cash

NAME ____________________

DATE ________ CLASS SECTION ________

CHATHAM CLOTHIERS, INC.
Income Statement
For the Year Ended December 31, 19X5

(in thousands)

CHATHAM CLOTHIERS, INC.
Statement of Retained Income
For the Year Ended December 31, 19X5
(in thousands)

CHATHAM CLOTHIERS, INC.
Balance Sheet
December 31, 19X5

(in thousands)

Assets

Current assets:

Equities

Current liabilities:

NAME ______________________

DATE ________ CLASS SECTION ________

Entry	Accounts and Explanation	Post Ref.	(in thousands) DR.	CR.

NAME ________________________

DATE ________ CLASS SECTION ________

Entry		Accounts and Explanation	Ref.	(in thousands) DR.	CR.

NAME ____________________________

DATE ________ CLASS SECTION ________

Entry		Accounts and Explanation	Ref.	(in thousands) DR.	CR.

The foldout multi-column work sheets which accompany Problems 5-24, 5-25, 5-26, and 5-27 can be found at the back of the book.

NAME ____________________

DATE ________ CLASS SECTION ________

Alternative Transaction Analysis

Entry		Accounts and Explanation	Post Ref.	DR. (in thousands)	CR. (in thousands)

Cash

3. Comments:

NAME ______________________________

DATE __________ CLASS SECTION __________

5-29	Debit	Credit	Amount
a.			
b.			
c.			
d.			
e.			
f.			
g.			
h.			
i.			

5-30 1. 2. 3. 4. 5.

5-31	19X1	19X2
1.		
2.		
3.		
4.		

5-32	19X1	19X2
a.		
b.		
c.		
d.		
e.		
f.		

NAME ______________________________

DATE __________ CLASS SECTION __________

Cash

R. U. BLUE CO.
Income Statement
For the Year Ended December 31, 19X1

NAME ____________________

DATE ________ CLASS SECTION ________

5-35 and 5-36

Accrual Basis of Accounting

5-35

JOSE CONSULTING ENGINEERS, INC.

Income Statement

For the Year Ended June 30, 19X4

5-35

JOSE CONSULTING ENGINEERS, INC.
Balance Sheet
June 30, 19X4

Assets

Current Assets:

Equities

Current Liabilities:

5-36 Cash Analysis:

NAME ______________________

DATE ________ CLASS SECTION ________

3. Company name:
4. Products, services:
5. Activity area:
6. Ending date of report:
7. Total assets:
8. Total liabilities:
9. Total stockholders' equity:
10. Total revenues:
11. Total expenses:
12. Net income:
13. Total dividends
14. EPS:
15. Dividends per share:
16. Stock market:
17. Market price:
18. Price-earnings ratio:
19. Dividend yield:
20. Dividend-payout ratio:
21. Independent accountants:
22. All amounts certified correct?

    If not, what did they say?

23. Number of shareholders:

24. Number of employees:

25. Number of pages:

26. Number of notes:

27. Chief executive officer:

28. Number of common shares:

29. Book value per share:

30. Years of comparative statistics:

31. Other terms used:

(a) For balance sheet:

(b) For income statement:

32. Your comments:

NAME ____________________

DATE ________ CLASS SECTION ________

	FIFO	LIFO	Weighted Average
Sales			
Less cost of goods sold:			
Inventory, December 31, 19X1			
Purchases			
Cost of goods available for sale			
Deduct inventory, December 31, 19X2 (computed below)			
Cost of goods sold			
Gross profit on sales			
Computations of inventory, Dec. 31, 19X2:			
FIFO:			
LIFO:			
Weighted average:			
Income tax differences:			

6-3 Effects of Late Purchases:

NAME ______________________________

DATE __________ CLASS SECTION __________

1.	19X1	19X2
Beginning inventory		
Ending inventory		
Cost of goods sold		
Gross profit		
Income before income taxes		
Income tax expense		
Net income		
2. Retained income effect at end of year:		

NAME ____________________

DATE ________ CLASS SECTION ________

	FIFO	LIFO	Weighted Average
Sales			
Less cost of goods sold:			
Beginning inventory			
Purchases			
Cost of goods available for sale			
Deduct ending inventory (computed below)			
Cost of goods sold			
Gross profit on sales			
Other expenses			
Income before income taxes			
Income taxes			
Net income			
Computations of ending inventory:			
FIFO:			
LIFO:			
Weighted average:			

NAME ______________________________

DATE __________ CLASS SECTION __________

NAME ____________________

DATE ________ CLASS SECTION ________

(in thousands)

NAME ____________________

DATE ________ CLASS SECTION ________

NAME ______________________

DATE ________ CLASS SECTION ________

6-26

1.

SERBEIN JEWELERS INC.
Statement of Gross Profit
For the Year Ended December 31, 19X3

2. Inventory turnover:

6-27

NAME ______________________________

DATE __________ CLASS SECTION __________

	19X5	19X4	19X3	19X2

NAME ____________________

DATE ________ CLASS SECTION ________

Replacement Cost, LIFO, FIFO

	Replacement Cost	LIFO	FIFO
1.			
2.			

NAME ______________________________

DATE ________ CLASS SECTION ________ LIFO or NIFO

	FIFO	LIFO	NIFO
1. Gross profit:			
2. Cash receipts and disbursements:			
Gross profit			
Deduct: Income taxes @ 40%			
Net income			
Sales			
Cash disbursements for:			
Income taxes			
Cash dividends equal to net income			
Sub-total			
Cash remaining for replenishment of inventory			
Cash needed to replace inventory			
Cash remaining (shortage)			
3. Summary of effects on cash position:			

NAME ____________________

DATE ________ CLASS SECTION ________

1. Statement of gross profit:	FIFO Cost		Lower of FIFO Cost or Market	
	19X1	19X2	19X1	19X2

2. Comments

NAME ____________________

DATE ________ CLASS SECTION ________

1. and 2. Computations:	LIFO	FIFO

2. Comments:

NAME ____________________

DATE ________ CLASS SECTION ________

1. LIFO (in thousands)	Do Not Buy	Buy More Units
2. FIFO		

3. Comments:

4. (a) (in thousands)	LIFO		FIFO	
	Do Not Buy	Buy	Do Not Buy	Buy

4. (b) (c) (d) (e) Comments:

NAME

DATE CLASS SECTION

1.

2.

3.

4. (a)

4. (b)

5.

NAME ____________________

DATE ________ CLASS SECTION ________

Eroding the LIFO Base

	(in thousands) Requirement 1.	Requirement 2.
Sales		
Cost of goods sold (computed below)		
Gross profit		
Operating expenses		
Income before income taxes		
Income taxes		
Net income		

Computations:

NAME ______________________

DATE __________ CLASS SECTION __________

6-41 or 6-42

LIFO Reserve and Liquidation

NAME ____________________

DATE ________ CLASS SECTION ________

Transaction	ASSETS: Plus or Minus Amount	ASSETS: Increase or Decrease Account	=	LIAB. 0	STOCKHOLDERS' EQUITY: Plus or Minus Amount	STOCKHOLDERS' EQUITY: Increase or Decrease Account
1. 19X2 Sales			=	0		
19X3 Writeoff			=	0		
2. 19X2 Sales			=	0		
19X2 Allowance			=	0		
19X3 Writeoff			=	0		

NAME ____________________

DATE ________ CLASS SECTION ________ Detailed Income Statement

JOHNSON BUILDING SUPPLY COMPANY

Income Statement

For the Year Ended December 31, 19X5

(in thousands)

Revenues:			
Gross sales			

NAME ______________________________

DATE ________ CLASS SECTION ________

GENERAL LEDGER

Accounts Receivable	

Allowance for Uncollectible Accounts	

SUBSIDIARY LEDGER

Ricks	

Vogel	

Parker	

Others	

Accounts Receivable
December 31, 19X4

Ricks	
Vogel	
Parker	
Others	
Total	

NAME ____________________

DATE ________ CLASS SECTION ________

Transaction	ASSETS		=	LIAB.	STOCKHOLDERS' EQUITY	
	Plus or Minus Amount	Increase or Decrease Account	=	0	Plus or Minus Amount	Increase or Decrease Account
Sales on Credit			=	0		
Returns and Allowances			=	0		
Cash Discounts			=	0		

Revenue Section of Income Statement

NAME ____________________

DATE ________ CLASS SECTION ________

Transaction	ASSETS		=	LIAB.	STOCKHOLDERS' EQUITY	
	Plus or Minus Amount	Increase or Decrease Account	=	0	Plus or Minus Amount	Increase or Decrease Account
			=	0		
			=	0		
			=	0		
			=	0		

NAME ______________________

DATE __________ CLASS SECTION __________

Transaction	ASSETS		=	LIAB.	STOCKHOLDERS' EQUITY	
	Plus or Minus Amount	Increase or Decrease Account	=	0	Plus or Minus Amount	Increase or Decrease Account
1. (a) Jan. 28 sale			=	0		
1. (a) Feb. 5 collection			=	0		
1. (b) Jan. 28 sale			=	0		
1. (b) Feb. 5 collection			=	0		
2. (a) Feb. 26 collection			=	0		
2. (b) Feb. 26 collection			=	0		

3. Method preference and reasons:

NAME ____________________

DATE ________ CLASS SECTION ________

HANDY HARDWARE WHOLESALERS
Statement of Gross Profit
For the Year Ended December 31, 19X8
(in thousands)

Gross sales:

NAME ______________________________

DATE ________ CLASS SECTION ________

Description Filter AG4

Cost flow assumption FIFO

Location ______________

Maximum ______________

Minimum ______________

Date	Units			Dollars			
	Purchased	Sold	Balance	Unit Cost	Purchased	Sold	Balance
19X1 Dec. 31							
19X2 Jan. 20							
Feb. 5							
May 20							
June 17							
Oct. 24							
Nov. 29							

7-28 Journal Entries

Transaction	Perpetual System			Periodic System		
Purchases						
Cost of Goods Sold						

Equation Analysis	ASSETS		=	LIAB.	SE
Transaction	Inventory	Purchases	=	Accounts Payable	Cost of Goods Sold
Perpetual System Bal. Dec. 31, 19X1			=		
			=		
			=		
			=		
Periodic System Bal. Dec. 31, 19X1			=		
			=		
			=		
			=		
			=		

NAME ______________________________

DATE __________ CLASS SECTION __________

EQUATION ANALYSIS	ASSETS			=	LIAB	SE
Transaction	Inventory	Purchases	Purchase Returns & Allowances	=	Accounts Payable	Cost of Goods Sold
Perpetual System Bal. Dec. 31, 19X1				=		
				=		
				=		
				=		
				=		
Periodic System Bal. Dec. 31, 19X1				=		
				=		
				=		
				=		
				=		
				=		

Journal Entries

Perpetual System:

Periodic System:

NAME ______________________________

DATE __________ CLASS SECTION __________

Inventory Destroyed by Fire

NAME ______________________

DATE __________ CLASS SECTION __________

NAME ______________________________

DATE ________ CLASS SECTION ________

Name	Total	1-30 days	31-60 days	61-90 days	Over 90 days

NAME ______________________

DATE ________ CLASS SECTION ________

Percentage of Accounts Receivable

Schedule:

End of Year	Receivables	Uncollectible	Recoveries
19X1			
19X2			
19X3			
19X4			
19X5			
19X6			
Total			
Average			

Computations:

Journal entry:

NAME ______________________

DATE ________ CLASS SECTION ________

NAME ______________________

DATE ________ CLASS SECTION ________

1. and 2.

ADRIAN COMPANY
Work Sheet (Perpetual Inventory System)
For the Year Ended December 31, 19X2

(in thousands)

Account Titles	Unadjusted Trial Balance		Adjustments		Income Statement		Statement of Retained Income		Balance Sheet	
	Dr.	Cr.	Dr.	Cr.	Dr.	Cr.	Dr.	Cr.	Dr.	Cr.
Cash	200									
Accounts Receivable	370									
Allow. for uncollect. accts.										
Merchandise inventory	500									
Equipment	400									
Accum. dep'n., eqpt.		100								
Accounts payable		400								
Income taxes payable										
Paid-in capital		100								
Retained inc., Dec. 31, 19X1		470								
Sales		2,300								
Sales Returns & allow.	100									
Cost of goods sold	1,400									
All other expenses	400									
	3,370	3,370								
Bad debt expense										
Income tax expense										
Net income										
Retained inc., Dec. 31, 19X2										

1. and 2.

(in thousands)

ADRIAN COMPANY
Work Sheet (Periodic Inventory System)
For the Year Ended December 31, 19X2

Account Titles	Unadjusted Trial Balance		Adjustments		Income Statement		Statement of Retained Income		Balance Sheet	
	Dr.	Cr.	Dr.	Cr.	Dr.	Cr.	Dr.	Cr.	Dr.	Cr.
Cash	200									
Accounts Receivable	370									
Allow. for uncollect. accts.										
Inventory, Dec. 31, 19X1	300									
Equipment	400									
Accum. depn., eqpt.		100								
Accounts payable		400								
Income taxes payable										
Paid-in capital		100								
Retained inc. Dec. 31, 19X1		470								
Sales		2,300								
Sales returns & allow.	100									
Purchases	1,690									
Purch. Returns & allow.		90								
All other expenses	400									
	3,460	3,460								
Bad debt expense										
Inventory, Dec. 31, 19X2										
Income tax expense										
Net income										
Retained inc., Dec. 31, 19X2										

3.

ADRIAN COMPANY
Income Statement
For the year ended December 31, 19x2
(in thousands)

	Perpetual System	Periodic System

4. Adjusting entries:	Perpetual Inventory System			Periodic Inventory System		
		Dr.	Cr.		Dr.	Cr.
j. Bad debts						
k. Ending inventory						
l. Income tax expense						
5. Closing entries:						
Revenue accounts						
Expense accounts						

NAME ____________________

DATE ________ CLASS SECTION ________

TRANSACTION	ASSETS	=	LIAB.	STOCKHOLDERS' EQUITY
1. Loans		=	0	
2. Write off		=	0	
3. Allowance		=	0	
4. Write off		=	0	

NAME ______________________________

DATE ________ CLASS SECTION ________

NAME ______________________

DATE ________ CLASS SECTION ________

1. Footnote:

2. Journal Entries (in thousands):

NAME ____________________

DATE __________ CLASS SECTION __________

1.

2. Ratios:

Journal Entries:

NAME ____________________

DATE ________ CLASS SECTION ________

(in millions)

1.			
Assets	=	Liabilities	Stockholders' Equity
	=		
	=		

Journal Entries:	Debit	Credit

2. Assets	=	Liabilities	Stockholders' Equity
	=		
	=		

Journal Entry:	Debit	Credit

NAME ______________________________

DATE __________ CLASS SECTION __________

7-44 and 7-45

Harrah's Casino Bad Debts

7-44: 1, 3, 4:

2. **Journal Entry:**

7-45: Journal Entries:

NAME ______________________________

DATE ________ CLASS SECTION ________

7-46: 1.

2.

7-47: Journal Entries:

Allowance for Uncollectibles

NAME ______________________

DATE ________ CLASS SECTION ________

NAME ______________________________

DATE __________ CLASS SECTION __________

NAME ______________________________

DATE __________ CLASS SECTION __________

1. and 2.

3. and 4.

NAME ______________________________

DATE ________ CLASS SECTION ________

		Journal Entries (Omit Explanations)		

8-31 (Continued)

Cash in Bank (Village Books)

Deposits (Bank Books)

VILLAGE OF LEWIS
Bank Reconciliation
March 31, 19X1

NAME ______________________________

DATE __________ CLASS SECTION __________

JOAN RIORDAN

Bank Reconciliation

October 31, 19X1

Journal Entry

NAME ______________________________

DATE __________ CLASS SECTION __________

NAME ____________________

DATE ________ CLASS SECTION ________

Sales Journal

page 42

Date	Account Debited	Invoice No.	Post	Dr. Accts. Rec. Cr. Sales

Cash Receipts Journal

page 63

Date	Account Credited	Explanation	Post	Other Accts. Credit	Accts. Rec. Credit	Sales Credit	Cash Debit

Cash Disbursements Journal

page 81

Date	Check No.	Payee	Account Debited	Post	Other Accts. Debit	Accts. Payable Debit	Mdse. Invent. Debit	Cash Credit

Purchases Journal

page 74

Date	Account Credited	Terms	Invoice Date	Post	Dr. Mdse. Invent. Cr. Accts. Pay.

General Journal

page 19

Date	Account Titles and Explanation	Post	Debit	Credit

2. GENERAL LEDGER

Cash	(10)

Accounts Receivable	(30)

Allowance for Bad Debts	(32)

Merchandise Inventory	(50)

Accounts Payable	(70)

Notes Payable	(75)

Property Taxes Payable	(77)

Paid-in Capital	(80)

Sales	(90)

Advertising Expense	(97)

Bad Debts Expense	(99)

SUBSIDIARY LEDGERS

Accounts Receivable

Haynes

Martin

Holford

Ramos

Lenz

Accounts Payable

Gates

Riggs

Goldman

Ryan

Hunter

3.

Accounts Receivable Ledger
List of Balances
July 31, 19X1

Name	Bal.

Accounts Payable Ledger
List of Balances
July 31, 19X1

Name	Bal.

4. Voucher System Effects:

NAME ______________________________

DATE __________ CLASS SECTION __________

Sales Journal

page 18

Date	Account Debited	Invoice	Post	Amount

Purchases Journal

page 14

Date	Account Credited	Terms	Post	Amount

Cash Receipts Journal

page 24

Date	Account Credited	Explanation	Post	Other Accts. Credit	Accts. Rec. Credit	Sales Credit	Sales Disct. Debit	Cash Debit

Cash Payments Journal

page 84

Date	Check No.	Payable to	Accounts Debited	Post	Other Accts. Debit	Accts. Pay. Debit	Purch. Debit	Purch. Disct. Credit	Cash Credit

General Journal

page 8

Date	Account Titles and Explanation	Post	Debit	Credit

SUBSIDIARY LEDGERS

Accounts Receivable

Alberto Co.	

Davidson, Inc.	

Barry & Thomas	

Wendell Bros.	

Accounts Payable

Austin Corp.	

Sydney, Inc.	

King & King	

Urban Stores, Inc.	

Raleigh Co.	

General Ledger

Cash (11)

Accounts Receivable (26)

Office Supplies (30)

Office Equipment (44)

Notes Payable (83)

Accounts Payable (82)

Sales (142)

Sales Ret. & Allow. (143)

Sales Discounts (144)

Purchases (162)

Purch. Ret. & Allow. (163)

Purchase Discounts (164)

All Other Accounts

General Ledger Trial Balance
August 31, 19X1

Schedule of Accounts Receivable
August 31, 19X1

Schedule of Accounts Payable
August 31, 19X1

NAME ____________________

DATE ________ CLASS SECTION ________

Comparison of Depreciation Methods

	Straight-Line		SYD Method		DDB Method	
	Annual Depreciation	Book Value	Annual Depreciation	Book Value	Annual Depreciation	Book Value
Acquisition cost						
Year 1						
2						
3						
4						
5						
Totals						
Computations:						

NAME ______________________

DATE __________ CLASS SECTION __________

SPEAS COMPANY ANALYSIS (in thousands)

	1. and 2.	ASSETS			=	L	SE	
	Transactions	Cash	Equip.	Accum. Dep'n.	=	Liab.	Paid-in Cap.	Retained Income
					=			
					=			
					=			
					=			
					=			
					=			
					=			
					=			
					=			
					=			
					=			
					=			
					=			
					=			
					=			
					=			
					=			
					=			
					=			
					=			
					=			
					=			
					=			
					=			
					=			

3. (a)

SPEAS COMPANY

Income Statement
For the Year Ended December 31, 19X2
(in thousands)

	Before Taxes		After Taxes	
	Straight Line Dep'n.	SYD Dep'n.	Straight Line Dep'n.	SYD Dep'n.

3. (b)

SPEAS COMPANY
Balance Sheet
December 31, 19x2
(in thousands)

Assets	Straight-Line Dep'n.	SYD Dep'n.	Equities	Straight-Line Dep'n.	SYD Dep'n.

4. and 5.

NAME ____________________________________

DATE __________ CLASS SECTION __________

1. Gain or loss:

Balance sheet equation:

ASSETS			=	L	SE
Cash	Equipment	Accumulated Depreciation	=	0	Gain on Sale
			=	0	

Income statement appearance:

9-4 (Continued)

NAME ______________________________ 9-24

DATE ________ CLASS SECTION ________ **Changes in Depreciation Estimates**

NAME ______________________

DATE ________ CLASS SECTION ________

	Straight-Line		SYD Method		DDB Method	
(in thousands)	Annual Depreciation	Book Value	Annual Depreciation	Book Value	Annual Depreciation	Book Value
Acquisition cost						
Year 1						
2						
3						
4						
5						
Totals						
Computations:						

NAME ______________________________ 9-28

DATE __________ CLASS SECTION __________ Basket Purchase

NAME ______________________________

DATE ________ CLASS SECTION ________

(in thousands)

Asset Year	Depreciation for 12-Month Periods	Allocation to Each Calendar Year					
		19X1	19X2	19X3	19X4	19X5	19X6

Computations:

NAME ____________________________________

DATE ________ CLASS SECTION ________

Comments:

Tabulation:

Original Depreciation		Revised Depreciation	
Year	Amount	Year	Amount

Computations:

NAME ______________________

DATE __________ CLASS SECTION __________

Y COMPANY

Balance Sheet

(Date)

Assets		Equities	

Comments:

NAME ______________________

DATE ________ CLASS SECTION ________

1, 2. (in thousands)	Part (1) 19x2	Change	19x3	Part (2) 19x2	Change	19x3

3. (in thousands)	Part (3a) 19x2	Change	19x3	Part (3b) 19x2	Change	19x3

4.

NAME ______________________________

DATE ________ CLASS SECTION ________

(in millions)

1. Analysis:	ASSETS				=	L	SE
Transactions and Events	Cash	Receivable from Ins. Co.	Flight Equip.	Accum. Dep'n.	=	Income Taxes Payable	Retained Income

1. Journal Entries:

2. Comments:

NAME ____________________

DATE ________ CLASS SECTION ________

(in thousands)

	Approach	
1.	(1a) Rams	(1b) IRS
2.	(2a) Initial Approach	(2b) Revised Approach
3. Comments:		

NAME ______________________________

DATE ________ CLASS SECTION ________

Land, Plant, and Equipment

Accumulated Depreciation

Unamortized Special Tools

Computations:

NAME ____________________________

DATE ________ CLASS SECTION ________

1.		Assets	=	Liabilities			SE
Date	Transaction	Cash	=	Accrued Wages Payable	Withheld Income Taxes Payable	Withheld Soc. Sec. Taxes Payable	Retained Income
			=				
			=				
			=				
			=				

2.

3.

NAME ______________________

DATE ________ CLASS SECTION ________

NAME ______________________________

DATE __________ CLASS SECTION __________

(in thousands)

1.	Assets		=	Liabilities		SE
Transactions	Cash	Investment in Bonds	=	Bonds Payable	Discount on Bonds Payable	Retained Income
Issuer's Records:						
(a)			=			
(b)			=			
(c)			=			
Totals			=			
Investor's Records:						
(a)			=			
(b)			=			
(c)			=			
Totals			=			

2. (in thousands)

3. (in thousands)

	December 31		
	1980	1987	1989
Issuer's Balance Sheet:			
Investor's Balance Sheet:			

NAME ______________________________

DATE ________ CLASS SECTION ________

1.		Gain or Loss (in thousands):		

2. Analysis **(in thousands)**

	Assets		=	Liabilities		SE
Transactions	**Cash**	**Investment in Bonds**	=	**Bonds Payable**	**Discount on Bonds Payable**	**Retained Income**
Issuer's Records:			=			
Investor's Records:			=			

2.		Journal Entries (in thousands):		
		Issuer's Records:		
		Investor's Records:		

NAME ____________________

DATE ________ CLASS SECTION ________

Analysis	ASSETS			=	LIABILITIES		SE
Transactions	Cash	Notes Receivable	Discount on Notes Receivable	=	Notes Payable	Discount on Notes Payable	Retained Income
Lender:							
				=			
				=			
				=			
				=			
Borrower:							
				=			
				=			
				=			
				=			

Lender's Entries:

Borrower's Entries:

NAME ______________________________

DATE ________ CLASS SECTION ________

	ASSETS	=	LIABILITIES	SE
Transaction	Cash	=	Sales Tax Payable	Sales
		=		
		=		
		=		

NAME ____________________

DATE ________ CLASS SECTION ________

(in thousands)

1.	ASSETS		=	LIABILITIES		SE
Transactions	Cash	Investment in Bonds	=	Bonds Payable	Premium on Bonds Payable	Retained Income
Issuer's Records:						
(a)			=			
(b)			=			
(c)			=			
Totals			=			
Investor's Records:						
(a)			=			
(b)			=			
(c)			=			
Totals			=			

2. (in thousands)

3. (in thousands)	December 31		
	1980	1987	1989
Issuer's Balance Sheet:			
Investor's Balance sheet:			

NAME ____________________

DATE ________ CLASS SECTION ________

(in thousands)

	ASSETS			=	LIABILITIES		SE
Date and Transaction	Cash	Notes Receivable	Accrued Interest Receivable	=	Note Payable	Accrued Interest Payable	Retained Income
Lender (Bank)							
Aug. 31, 19X1				=			
Dec. 31, 19X1				=			
Aug. 31, 19X2				=			
Borrower (Hospital)							
Aug. 31, 19X1				=			
Dec. 31, 19X1				=			
Aug. 31, 19X2				=			

NAME ________________________________

DATE __________ CLASS SECTION __________

(in thousands)

Year	Co.	(1) Assets	(2) Bonds Payable	(3) SE	(4) Income Before Interest	(5) 10% Interest	(6) (4) − (5) Net Income	(7) (4) ÷ (1) Return on Assets	(8) (6) ÷ (3) Return on SE
1	X								
1	Y								
2	X								
2	Y								
3	X								
3	Y								

Comments on the Results:

NAME ______________________

DATE __________ CLASS SECTION __________

1.

	(in thousands) $20,000 Issue Long-term Debt	Preferred Stock
Income before interest expense		
2. Ratios:		

NAME ______________________________

DATE ________ CLASS SECTION ________

Claims (in thousands)		Distribution of Proceeds (in thousands)	

NAME ____________________

DATE ________ CLASS SECTION ________

1. Computation of total proceeds:

2. Transaction analysis (in thousands)

	Assets			=	Liabilities		SE
Transactions and Dates	Cash	Investment in Bonds	Accrued Interest Receivable	=	Bonds Payable	Accrued Interest Payable	Retained Income
Issuer's Records:							
				=			
				=			
Investor's Records:							
				=			
				=			

2. Journal Entries (in thousands)

Date	Issuer's Records	Dr.	Cr.	Investor's Records	Dr.	Cr.

NAME ____________________

DATE ________ CLASS SECTION ________

1. Computation of issuance price:

3. Amortization schedule:

	Six Months Ended	Effective Interest	Nominal Interest	Discount Amortized	Unamortized Discount	Net Liability

	DR.	CR.
3. Journal entry:		

4. Comparison schedule:

Period	Effective Interest Amortization	Straight-Line Amortization
1		
2		
3		
4		
5		
6		
Total		

NAME ______________________________

DATE __________ CLASS SECTION __________

1. Computations:

2. Annual Journal Entry:

3. Analytical Schedule of Lease Payments

	(1)	(2)	(3) (1) + (2)	(4)	(5) (3) − (4)	(6) Same as (2)	(7) (4) − (2)
						Supplementary Analysis of Each Payment	
End of Year	Lease Liability at Beginning of Year	Interest at 16% Per Year	Accumulated Amount at End of Year	Cash for Lease Payment	Lease Liability at End of Year	Interest Expense	Reduction in Beginning Lease Liability
1							
2							
3							
Totals							

4. Analysis of Transactions Accounting for a Capital Lease

	ASSETS		=	LIABILITIES	SE
Transactions	Cash	Equipment Leasehold	=	Lease Liability	Retained Income
Signing of lease			=		
Lease payment End Year 1			=		
Lease payment End Year 2			=		
Lease payment End Year 3			=		
Amortization End Year 1			=		
Amortization End Year 2			=		
Amortization End Year 3			=		
Cumulative Totals			=		

4. Journal Entries

Accounts	Amounts		
	Year 1	Year 2	Year 3

NAME ______________________

DATE ________ CLASS SECTION ________

Computations:

NAME ______________________________

DATE __________ CLASS SECTION __________

10-37 Analysis:

	ASSETS	=	LIABILITIES	SE
Transaction	Cash	=	Accrued Pensions Payable	Retained Income
		=		

NAME ____________________

DATE ________ CLASS SECTION ________

1. Computations:

2.		Journal Entries:		

NAME ______________________________

DATE __________ CLASS SECTION __________

Polaroid Purchase Commitments

Equation Analysis (in millions)	ASSETS	=	LIABILITIES		SE
Transaction	Inventory	=	Reserve for Purchase Commitments	Accounts Payable	Retained Income
(1)		=			
(2)(a)		=			
(2)(b)		=			

NAME ______________________

DATE __________ CLASS SECTION __________

1. and 2.

Accumulated Depreciation

Properties and Plants

Long-Term Debt

Computations:

3. Journal entry:

NAME ______________________________

DATE ________ CLASS SECTION ________

Property, Plant and Equipment

Accumulated Depreciation

Long-Term Debt

Unamortized Debt Discount

NAME ______________________________

DATE __________ CLASS SECTION __________

1. Computations:

2.		Journal Entries:		

NAME

DATE   CLASS SECTION

1.

2, 3, 4. Journal Entries

5, 6. Use reverse side, if necessary.

NAME ______________________________

DATE ________ CLASS SECTION ________

RAMIREZ CORPORATION
Statement of Stockholders' Equity
December 31, 19X3

(in thousands)

NAME ______________________________

DATE __________ CLASS SECTION __________

1.		Journal Entry (in thousands)		

	(in thousands)		
2. Description	Before	Changes	After
3.			

3.		Journal Entry (in thousands):		
4.		Journal Entry:		

NAME ______________________________

DATE __________ CLASS SECTION __________

Journal Entries:

(in thousands)

Description	Before	Changes	After

NAME ______________________________

DATE ________ CLASS SECTION ________

	(in thousands)		
Description	Before	Changes	After

Journal Entries (in thousands):

NAME ______________________________

DATE ________ CLASS SECTION ________

Year	Net Income	Preferred Dividends Declared	Preferred Dividends in Arrears	Common Dividends Declared
19X1	$(5,000,000)			
19X2	(4,000,000)			
19X3	14,000,000			
19X4	30,000,000			
19X5	15,000,000			

Computations:

NAME ______________________________

DATE __________ CLASS SECTION __________

(in thousands)

Accounts	Account Balance	Total Cash Proceeds to be Distributed						
		$1,400	$1,000	$790	$500	$400	$200	$100
Totals								

NAME ______________________________

DATE __________ CLASS SECTION __________

Rate of return on common equity:

Earnings per share of common stock:

Price-earnings ratio:

Dividend-payout ratio:

Dividend-yield ratio:

Book value per share of common stock:

NAME ______________________________

DATE ________ CLASS SECTION ________

1. (in millions of dollars)

	Before Dividends	After Dividend Payments of:	
		(a) 7	(b) 3
Paid-in capital	40		
Retained income	7		
Total	47		
Deduct cost of treasury stock	4		
Stockholders' equity	43		

2. Comments: ______________________________

NAME ______________________________

DATE ________ CLASS SECTION ________

(in thousands)

NAME ______________________

DATE ________ CLASS SECTION ________

NAME ______________________

DATE ________ CLASS SECTION ________

(in thousands)

1. Equation Analysis:	ASSETS			=	LIAB.	STOCKHOLDERS' EQUITY	
J's Books:		Equipment		=		Common Stock	Additional Paid-in Capital
Issuance of stock by J				=	0		
K's Books:	Investment in J Common Stock	Equipment	Accumulated Depreciation	=			Retained Income
Disposal of Equipment by K				=	0		

2. Journal Entries:

On Issuer's Books	DR.	CR.	On Investor's Books	DR.	CR.

NAME ______________________

DATE ________ CLASS SECTION ________

(in thousands)

1. Equation Analysis	ASSETS			=	Liab.	STOCKHOLDERS' EQUITY			
Company H's Books:	Cash			=		Preferred Stock	Additional Paid-in Capital Preferred	Common Stock	Additional Paid-in Capital Common
				=	0				
				=	0				
Company G's Books:	Cash	Investment in H Preferred	Investment in H Common	=	0				
				=	0				
				=	0				

2. Journal Entries:

On Issuer's Books	DR.	CR.	On Investor's Books	DR.	CR.

NAME ____________________

DATE __________ CLASS SECTION __________

(in thousands)

	Dr.	Cr.

Comments:

NAME ______________________________

DATE __________ CLASS SECTION __________

Distinction between Fund and Reserve

1. and 2.

3.

Sinking Fund

Retained Earnings

Bonds Payable

Reserve for Sinking Fund

NAME ______________________________

DATE __________ CLASS SECTION __________

THE MERCKER COMPANY

Partial Income Statement

For the Year Ended December 31, 19X2

(in millions)

NAME ______________________________

DATE ________ CLASS SECTION ________

(in thousands)			
Description	Before	Changes	After

Computations:

		Journal Entry (in thousands):		

NAME ____________________

DATE ________ CLASS SECTION ________

(Dollar amounts in thousands)

1.	Common Shares	Common Amount	Addit. Pd.-in Capital	Retained Earnings	Total
Bal., May 31, 1978					
(a) 3-for-1 stock distribution					
(b) 10% stock dividend					
(c) Cash for fractional shares					
(d) Issuance of common stock					
(e) Exercise of stock options					
(f) Net earnings					
Bal., May 31, 1979					

Computations:

2. Journal Entries (in thousands):

NAME ______________________

DATE ________ CLASS SECTION ________

1., 2., 3. and 4.

5. Journal Entries:

NAME ______________________

DATE ________ CLASS SECTION ________

2. Comments:

NAME ____________________

DATE ________ CLASS SECTION ________

(in millions)

Equation Analysis	Equity Method					Cost Method				
	Assets		=	Equities		Assets		=	Equities	
Transaction	Cash	Invest.	=	Liab.	SE	Cash	Invest.	=	Liab.	SE
1. Acquisition			=					=		
2. Net income of E			=					=		
3. Dividends from E			=					=		
Effects for year			=					=		

Journal Entries:

Equity Method:

1.

2.

3.

Cost Method:

1.

2.

3.

NAME ____________________

DATE ________ CLASS SECTION ________

1. (in millions)

Equation Analysis	Assets		=	Liab.	SE
Explanation	Investment in S	Cash and Other Assets	=	Accounts Payable, etc.	Stkhldrs'. Equity
P's accounts before acquisition, Jan. 1			=		
Acquisition of S			=		
S's accounts, Jan. 1			=		
Intercompany eliminations			=		
Consolidated bal., Jan. 1			=		

2. (in millions)

Income Statement	Co. P.	Co. S.	Consolidated
Sales			
Expenses			
Operating income			
Share of subsid. net income			
Net income			

3. (in millions)

Equation Analysis	Assets		=	Liab.	SE
	Investment in S	Cash and Other Assets	=	Accounts Payable, etc.	Stkhldrs'. Equity
P's Accounts:					
Beginning of year			=		
Operating income			=		
Share of S income			=		
End of year			=		
S's Accounts:					
Beginning of year			=		
Net income			=		
End of year			=		
Intercompany eliminations			=		
Consolidated bal., end of year			=		

4. Comments

NAME ____________________

DATE ________ CLASS SECTION ________

1. (in millions)

Equation Analysis	Assets		=	Liabilities + SE		
	Investment in S	Cash and Other Assets	=	Accounts Pay., etc.	Minority Interest	SE
P's accounts before acquisition, Jan. 1.			=			
Acquisition of S			=			
S's accounts, Jan. 1			=			
Interco. eliminations			=			
Consolidated bal., Jan. 1.			=			

2. (in millions)

Income Statement	Co. P.	Co. S.	Consolidated
Sales			
Expenses			
Operating income			
Share of subsid. net income			
Net income			
Minority interest in net income			
Consolidated net income			

3. (in millions)

Equation Analysis	Assets		=	Liabilities + SE		
	Investment in S	Cash and Other Assets	=	Accounts Payable, etc.	Minority Interest	SE
P's Accounts:						
Beginning of year			=			
Operating income			=			
Share of S income			=			
End of year			=			
S's Accounts:						
Beginning of year			=			
Net income			=			
End of year			=			
Interco. eliminations			=			
Consolidated, end of year			=			

4. Comments:

NAME ______________________________

DATE __________ CLASS SECTION __________

1. (in millions)

Equation Analysis	Assets		=	Liabilities	SE
	Investment in S	Cash and Other Assets	=	Accounts Payable, etc.	SE
P's accounts before acquisition, Jan. 1			=		
Acquistion of S			=		
S's accounts Jan. 1			=		
Interco. eliminations			=		
Consolidated, Jan. 1			=		

2. ______________________________

____

3. (a) ______________________________

____

____

____

____

____

3. (b) ______________________________

____

____

____

____

____

____

____

____

____

____

____

____

____

NAME ______________________________

DATE __________ CLASS SECTION __________

Short-term Investment Portfolio

1. Tabulations (in millions):

Balance Sheet:

Income Statement:

2. Journal Entries (in millions):

NAME ____________________

DATE ________ CLASS SECTION ________

LUMSDEN CORPORATION
Consolidated Income Statement
For the Year Ended December 31, 19X2

(in millions)

LUMSDEN CORPORATION
Consolidated Balance Sheet
December 31, 19x2
(in millions)

Assets		Equities	

NAME ______________________________

DATE __________ CLASS SECTION __________

(in millions)

	Assets		=	Equities	
	Cash	Investment	=	Liab.	SE
Equity Method:					
Acquisition			=		
Net income of B			=		
Dividends from B			=		
Effects for the year			=		
Cost of Method:					
Acquisition			=		
Net income of B			=		
Dividends from B			=		
Effects for the year			=		

NAME ______________________

DATE __________ CLASS SECTION __________

1.

(in millions)

Equation Analysis	Assets		=	Liab.	SE
Explanation	Investment in S	Cash and Other Assets	=	Accounts Payable, etc.	Stkhldrs'. Equity
P's accounts before acquisition, Jan. 1			=		
Acquisition of S			=		
S's accounts, Jan. 1			=		
Intercompany eliminations			=		
Consolidated bal., Jan. 1			=		

2.

(in millions)

Income Statement	Co. P.	Co. S.	Consolidated
Sales			
Expenses			
Operating income			
Share of subsid. net income			
Net income			

3.

(in millions)

Equation Analysis	Assets		=	Liab.	SE
	Investment in S	Cash and Other Assets	=	Accounts Payable, etc.	Stkhldrs'. Equity
P's Accounts:					
Beginning of year			=		
Operating income			=		
Share of S income			=		
End of year			=		
S's Accounts:					
Beginning of year			=		
Net income			=		
End of year			=		
Intercompany eliminations			=		
Consolidated bal., end of year			=		

4. Comments

NAME ______________________________

DATE __________ CLASS SECTION __________

D COMPANY
Consolidated Income Statement
For the Year Ended December 31, 19X4

(in thousands)

D COMPANY
Consolidated Balance Sheet
December 31, 19X4
(in thousands)

Assets

Equities

NAME ______________________

DATE ________ CLASS SECTION ________

1.

(in millions)

Income Statement	Co. P.	Co. S.	Consolidated
Sales			
Expenses			
Operating income			
Share of subsid. net income			
Net income			

(in millions)

Balance Sheet	Assets		=	Liab.	SE
	Investment in S	Cash and Other Assets	=	Accounts Payable, etc.	Stkhldrs'. Equity
P's Accounts:					
Beginning of year			=		
Operating income			=		
Share of S income			=		
End of year			=		
S's Accounts:					
End of year			=		
Intercompany eliminations			=		
Consolidated bal., end of year			=		

2.

(in millions)

Income Statement	Co. P.	Co. S.	Consolidated
Sales			
Expenses			
Operating income			
Share of subsid. net income			
Net income			
Minority interest in net income			
Consol. net income			

(in millions)

Balance Sheet	Assets		=	Equities		
	Invest. in S	Cash, etc.	=	Accts. Pay., etc.	Minority Interest	Stk. Eq.
P's Accounts:						
Beginning of year						
Operating income						
Share of S income						
End of year						
S's Accounts, end of year						
Intercompany eliminations						
Consolidated, end of year						

NAME ________________________________

DATE ________ CLASS SECTION ________

12-30 (in millions)

1. Balance Sheet	Assets				=	SE	
	Cash	Invent.	Plant Assets	Invest. in Y	=	Pd.-in Cap.	RI
X's Accounts:							
Before acquisition					=		
Acquisition					=		
Y's Accounts					=		
Interco. eliminations					=		
Consolidated					=		

2. and 3. Comments:

12-31 Amortization and Depreciation

(1)

(2)

NAME ____________________

DATE ________ CLASS SECTION ________

1.

GREYMONT
Consolidated Balance Sheet
December 31, 19x1
(in millions)

Assets		Equities	

2. ____________________

NAME ______________________

DATE ________ CLASS SECTION ________

(in millions)

Balance Sheet	Assets		=	Liabilities + SE		
	Investment Subsidiaries	Other Assets	=	Accts. Payable	Minority Interests	SE
Parent's accounts			=			
S-1 accounts			=			
S-2 accounts			=			
Interco. eliminations:						
S-1			=			
S-2			=			
Consolidated			=			

(in millions)

Income Statement	Parent	S-1	S-2	Consol.
Sales				
Expenses				
Income before minority				
Minority interests				
Consol. net income				

NAME ____________________

DATE ________ CLASS SECTION ________

(in millions)

Balance Sheets	Assets		=	Liabilities + SE		
	Invest-ment in S	Other Assets	=	Accts. Payable	Minority Interest	SE
P's accounts			=			
S's accounts			=			
Interco. eliminations			=			
Consolidated		141	=	55	10	

Computations:

(in millions)

Income Statements	Co. P	Co. S	Consol.
Sales	301		371
Expenses			360
Income before minority			
Minority interest			2
Consolidated net income			

(in millions)

1. Purchase Method	Assets		=	Equities	
	Invest. in S	Cash and Other Assets	=	Liab.	SE
P's accounts:					
Before stock issuance			=		
Stock issuance			=		
Acquisition of S			=		
S's accounts			=		
Interco. eliminations			=		
Consolidated			=		

2. Pooling Method (in millions)

P's accounts:					
Before acquisition			=		
Acquisition of S			=		
S's accounts			=		
Interco. eliminations			=		
Consolidated			=		

3. Comments:

NAME ______________________________

DATE ________ CLASS SECTION ________

(in millions)

1. (a) Purchase Method	Assets		=	Liab. + SE	
	Invest. in S	Cash and Other Assets	=	Accts. Payable	SE
B's accounts:					
Before acquisition			=		
Acquisition of Y			=		
Y's accounts			=		
Interco. eliminations			=		
Consolidated			=		

1. (b) Pooling Method

(in millions)

B's accounts:					
Before acquisition			=		
Acquisition of Y			=		
Y's accounts			=		
Interco. eliminations			=		
Consolidated			=		

2. (a)

2. (b)

3.

NAME ______________________________ 12-42

DATE ________ CLASS SECTION ________ Transaction Effects, Equity Method

1. Investment in Affiliated Companies

2.

NAME ____________________

DATE ________ CLASS SECTION ________

1. Intangibles Arising from Business Acquisitions

2. Marketable Securities (at cost)

3. Valuation Allowances

NAME ______________________

DATE ________ CLASS SECTION ________

(in thousands)

1 and 2.	Assets		=	Liabilities		SE	
Transaction	Cash	Equip.	=	Inc. Tax Payable	Deferred Invest. Tax Credit	Paid-in Capital	Ret. Inc.
(a) Formation			=				
(b) Operation			=				
(c) Acquire equip.			=				
(d) Income taxes			=				
Bal., Dec. 31, 19x1			=				
(e) 1. Flow through			=				
Bal. after (e) 1.			=				
(e) 2. Deferral			=				
Bal. after (e) 2.			=				

3. (d)

(a)

(b)

4. (a)

(b)

NAME ____________________

DATE ________ CLASS SECTION ________

(in millions)

1.	Assets		=	Liabilities		SE	
Transaction	Cash	Equip.	=	Inc. Tax Payable	Deferred Invest. Tax Credit	Paid-in Capital	Ret. Inc.
(a) Formation			=				
(b) Acquire equip.			=				
(c) Income before dep'n.			=				
(d) Straight-line dep'n.			=				
(e) 1. Inc. tax expense			=				
Bal. after (e) 1.			=				
(e) 2. Inc. tax expense			=				
Bal. after (e) 2.			=				

Computations:

(in millions)

2.	Year One Reporting		
		To Shareholders	
	To Income Tax Authorities	No Deferral	Deferral
Income before depreciation and taxes			
Depreciation:			
SYD			
Straight-line			
Income before income taxes			
Income tax expense:			
Paid or payable almost immediately			
Deferred			
Total income tax expense			
Net income			

NAME ____________________

DATE ________ CLASS SECTION ________

(in millions)

1. Reporting on Income Tax Returns

Year	Income Before Depreciation and Taxes	SYD Depreciation	Income Before Tax	Income Tax Paid or Payable Soon	Net Income
1					
2					
3					
4					
5					
Total					

2. (a) Reporting to Stockholders: Straight-line Depreciation and No Tax Deferral (Outlawed)

Year	Income Before Depreciation and Taxes	Straight-Line Depreciation	Income Before Tax	Income Tax Expense	Net Income
1					
2					
3					
4					
5					
Total					

2. (b) Reporting to Stockholders: Straight-line Depreciation and Tax Deferral (Required)

Year	Income Before Dep'n. & Taxes	Straight-Line Dep'n.	Income Before Tax	Income Tax Expense			Net Income	Balance Sheet: Deferred Inc. Tax
				Tax Paid	Tax Deferred	Total Tax Expense		
1								
2								
3								
4								
5								
Total					–0–			–0–

NAME ______________________

DATE ________ CLASS SECTION ________

(in millions)

1. Reporting for Tax Purposes: SYD Depreciation

Year	Income Before Dep'n. and Taxes	SYD Depreciation	Income Before Tax	Income Tax Paid	Net Income
1					
2					
3					
4					
5					
6					

Computations:

(in millions)

2. Reporting to Stockholders: Straight-Line Depreciation and Tax Allocation

Year	Income Before Dep'n. and Taxes	Straight-Line Dep'n.	Income Before Tax	Income Tax Expense			Net Income	Balance Sheet: Deferred Inc. Tax
				Tax Paid	Tax Deferred	Total Tax Expense		
1								
2								
3								
4								
5								
6								

NAME ______________________

DATE __________ CLASS SECTION __________

1. Computations:

		2. (a)	
		(b)	

3. ______________________________

NAME ______________________________

DATE ________ CLASS SECTION ________

Amortization Schedule: Investment Credit

(in thousands)

	(1)	(2)	(3) (1) + (2)	(4)	(5) (1) + (4)
Year of Use	Net inc. Before Effect of Invest. Credit	Recognized Immediately	Net Income	Amortization	Net Income
Acquisition					
1					
2					
3					
4					
5					
6					
7					
8					
Total					

NAME ______________________________

DATE ________ CLASS SECTION ________

NAME ____________________

DATE ________ CLASS SECTION ________

(in thousands)

		(1)	(2)	(3) (1) + (2)	(4)	(5)	(6) (1) + (5)	(7)
	Year	Avg. Net Inc. Before Invest Credit	Flow-Through	Avg. Net Income	Earnings Per Share	Deferral	Avg. Net Income	Earnings Per Share
1.	1							
	2							
	3							
	4							
	Etc.							
2.	1							
	2							
	3							
	4							
	Etc.							
3.	1							
	2							
	3							
	4							
	Etc.							

4. (Over)

4.

NAME ____________________

DATE ________ CLASS SECTION ________

(in millions)

Reporting for Tax Purposes: SYD Depreciation					
Year	Income Before Dep'n. and Taxes	SYD Depreciation	Income Before Tax	Income Tax Paid	Net Income
7					

Computations:

(in millions)

Reporting to Stockholders: Straight-Line Depreciation and Tax Allocation								
				Income Tax Expense				
Year	Income Before Dep'n. and Taxes	Straight-Line Dep'n.	Income Before Tax	Tax Paid	Tax Deferred	Total Tax Expense	Net Income	Bal. Sheet: Deferred Inc. Tax
7								

NAME ____________________

DATE ________ CLASS SECTION ________

(in thousands)

1. Reporting for Tax Purposes: SYD Depreciation					
Year	Income Before Dep'n. and Taxes	SYD Depreciation	Income Before Tax	Income Tax Paid	Net Income
1					
2					
3					
4					
5					
6					

Computations:

(in thousands)

1. Reporting to Stockholders:
Straight-Line Depreciation and Tax Allocation

Year	Income Before Dep'n. and Taxes	Straight-Line Dep'n.	Income Before Tax	Income Tax Expense			Net Income	Bal. Sheet: Deferred Inc. Tax
				Tax Paid	Tax Deferred	Total Tax Expense		
1								
2								
3								
4								
5								
6								

2. ____________________

NAME ______________________________

DATE ________ CLASS SECTION ________

(in thousands except EPS)

	(1) and (2b)	(2a)
Income before dep'n. on new assets		
Depreciation		
Income before income tax		
Income taxes:		
Before investment credit		
Less investment credit		
Net income		
Earnings per share		

	(2c)	(2d)
Income before dep'n. on new assets		
Depreciation		
Income before income tax		
Income taxes:		
Tax paid		
Tax deferred because of:		
DDB depreciation		
Deferral of invest. credit		
Net income		
Earnings per share		

NAME ______________________

DATE __________ CLASS SECTION __________

1.

	Year	Pre-Tax Gross Profit	Income Tax Expense			Net Income	Bal. of Deferred Inc. Tax
			Tax Paid	Tax Deferred	Total Tax Expense		
2.	1						
	2						
	3						
3.	1						
	2						
	3						
	4						
	5						
4.	1						
	2						
	3						
	4						
	5						

Computations:

5. (Over)

5.

NAME ____________________

DATE ________ CLASS SECTION ________

(in thousands)

1. Analysis	Cash and Other Assets	=	Liabilities	Owners' Equity				
				Behling, Capital		Behling, Drawings		Income Summary
Proprietorship:								
Initial investment		=	0					
Revenue		=	0					
Expenses		=	0					
Withdrawals		=	0					
Transfer net income to capital		=	0					
End. bal., 12-31-X2		=	0					
				Behling, Capital	Miller, Capital	Behling, Drawings	Miller, Drawings	Income Summary
Partnership:								
Initial investment		=	0					
Revenues		=	0					
Expenses		=	0					
Withdrawals		=	0					
Transfer net income to capital		=	0					
End. bal., 12-31-X2		=	0					

2. (in thousands)

NAME ______________________________

DATE ________ CLASS SECTION ________

NAME ____________________

DATE ________ CLASS SECTION ________

NAME ______________________________

DATE ________ CLASS SECTION ________

1.

PEAT MARWICK INTERNATIONAL
Income Statement
(Year)

(in millions)		

2. ______________________________

NAME ______________________________

DATE __________ CLASS SECTION __________

1.

		2. (in thousands)		

3. ______________________________

____

____

4.

NAME ______________________

DATE ________ CLASS SECTION ________

	Nominal Dollars				Constant Dollars			
	Historical Cost		Current Cost		Historical Cost		Current Cost	
Balance Sheets, Dec. 31:	19X4	19X5	19X4	19X5	19X4	19X5	19X4	19X5
Cash								
Income Statement, 19X5:								
Sales								

Computations (continue on other side):

NAME ______________________________

DATE __________ CLASS SECTION __________

1.

Land Acquired	(a) Traditionally Recorded Costs	(b) Expressed in 1981 Dollars	(c) Expressed in 1971 Dollars	(d) Expressed in 1961 Dollars
1961				
1981				
Total				

Computations:

2. Explanations:

NAME ______________________________

DATE __________ CLASS SECTION __________

	Historical Cost		Current Cost (Specific Price Level)	
	(1)	(2)	(3)	(4)
1.	Not Restated	Restated for General Price Level Effects	Not Restated	Restated for General Price Level Effects
Dec. 31, 19X4 Balance Sheet:	19X3 Dollars	19X4 Dollars	19X4 Dollars	19X4 Dollars
Land				
Equity:				
Original capital				
Retained earnings				
19X4 Income Statement:				
Gain				
2.	19X5 Dollars	19X5 Dollars	19X5 Dollars	19X5 Dollars
Dec. 31, 19X5 Balance Sheet:				
Cash				
Land				
Equity:				
Original capital				
Retained earnings				
19X5 Income Statement:				
Gain				

3. Explanations:

NAME ____________________

DATE ________ CLASS SECTION ________

1. Year	Adjusted Depreciation As Recorded	Multiplier	Adjusted Depreciation in Dollars of Fourth Year
1			
2			
3			
4			

2.

3.

4.

NAME ____________________

DATE ________ CLASS SECTION ________

	In 19X2 Dollars	
	19X1	19X2

NAME ____________________

DATE ________ CLASS SECTION ________

	(1)	(2)	(3)
1.	Measured in 19X3 Purchasing Power	Measured in 19X4 Purchasing Power	As Conventionally Measured
Cash bal., Dec. 31, 19X3			
Cash bal., Dec. 31, 19X4			
Purchasing power loss			
2.			
Land bal., Dec. 31, 19X3			
Land bal., Dec. 31, 19X4			
Purchasing power loss			

NAME ______________________________

DATE ________ CLASS SECTION ________

1.	Historical Cost and Nominal Dollars		Historical Cost and Constant Dollars	
Balance sheets:	One Year Ago	Today	One Year Ago	Today
Cash				
Gov't. bonds				
Land				
Total assets				
Stockholders' equity				
Income Statements:				
Rev. less exp.	X		X	
Purch. power loss on monetary assets	X		X	
Net change in stockholders' equity	X		X	

2. ______________________________

NAME ____________________

DATE ________ CLASS SECTION ________

	Nominal Dollars				Constant Dollars			
	Historical Cost		Current Cost		Historical Cost		Current Cost	
Balance Sheets, Dec. 31:	19X1	19X2	19X1	19X2	19X1	19X2	19X1	19X2
Cash								
Income Statement, 19X2:								
Sales								

Computations (continue on other side):

NAME ______________________

DATE ________ CLASS SECTION ________

Extension of Appendix Problem

	Nominal Dollars				Constant Dollars			
	Historical Cost		Current Cost		Historical Cost		Current Cost	
Balance Sheets, Dec. 31:	19X1	19X2	19X1	19X2	19X1	19X2	19X1	19X2
Cash								
Income Statement, 19X2:								
Sales								

Computations (continue on other side):

NAME ______________________________

DATE ________ CLASS SECTION ________

BARBER-ELLIS OF CANADA, LIMITED
1974 Annual Report

NAME ______________________ 15-2

DATE ________ CLASS SECTION ________ **Prepare Statement**

1.

G COMPANY

Statement of Changes in Financial Position (Working Capital)

For the Year Ended December 31, 19X3

(in thousands)

Sources and Uses of Working Capital

Sources:

Changes in Components of Working Capital

	Dec. 31 19X3	Dec. 31 19X2	Increase (Decrease)
Current assets:			

Working Capital Provided by Operations

2.

3. (in thousands)	ΔWC =	ΔNCL +	ΔPC +	ΔRI −	ΔNCA

NAME ______________________________

DATE ________ CLASS SECTION ________ Prepare Statement

1.

WEINBERG CO.
Statement of Changes in Financial Position
For the Year Ended December 31, 19X2

(in millions)

Sources and Uses of Working Capital

Sources:

Changes in Components of Working Capital

	Dec. 31 19X2	Dec. 31 19X1	Increase (Decrease)
Current assets:			

2.

WEINBERG CO.
Statement of Sources of Working Capital
For the Year Ended December 31, 19X2

(in millions)		
Sales		

3, 4.

5. (in millions)	ΔWC =	ΔNCL +	ΔPC +	ΔRE –	ΔNCA

NAME ______________________

DATE ________ CLASS SECTION ________

DYLE COMPANY

	Part 1	Part 2

NAME ____________________________ 15-24

DATE ________ CLASS SECTION ________ Items Not Affecting Working Capital

NAME ____________________

DATE ________ CLASS SECTION ________

D COMPANY

Statement of Changes in Financial Position

For the Year Ended December 31, 19x4

(in millions)

NAME ______________________________

DATE __________ CLASS SECTION __________

1.

DENNY COMPANY

Statement of Changes in Financial Position

For the Year Ended December 31, 19X7

(in millions)

Sources and Applications of Working Capital

Changes in Components of Working Capital

	Dec. 31 19X7	Dec. 31 19X6	Increase (Decrease)

2.

NAME ______________________

DATE ________ CLASS SECTION ________

QUICK MANUFACTURING CO.
Statement of Changes in Financial Position
For the Year Ended December 31, 19X2

Sources and Uses of Working Capital

Changes in Components of Working Capital

	Dec. 31 19X1	Dec. 31 19X2	Increase (Decrease)

NAME ______________________________

DATE __________ CLASS SECTION __________

GOLIATH CORPORATION
Consolidated Statement of Changes in Financial Position
For the Year Ended December 31, 19x3

(in thousands)

Sources and Uses of Working Capital

15-29 (Continued)

Changes in Components of Working Capital

(in millions)			
	Dec. 31 19X3	Dec. 31 19X2	Increase (Decrease)

NAME ______________________________

DATE ________ CLASS SECTION ________

BURETTA CO.

Working Capital

Fixed Assets, Net

Mortgage Payable

Capital Stock

Retained Earnings

NAME ____________________

DATE ________ CLASS SECTION ________

Working Capital

Plant Assets, Net

Long-Term Debt

Stockholders' Equity

NAME ______________________________

DATE ________ CLASS SECTION ________

Working Capital

Plant Assets, Net

Mortgage Payable

Capital Stock

Retained Earnings

NAME ______________________________

DATE __________ CLASS SECTION __________

Working Capital

Fixed Assets

Accumulated Depreciation

Patents

4% Serial Bonds

Capital Stock

Additional Paid-in Capital

Retained Earnings

NAME ____________________________

DATE ________ CLASS SECTION ________

1. DRIVO COMPANY

(in thousands except EPS)

	(1)	(2) FIFO	(3) Straight-Line	(4) Amortization	(5) Flow-Through	(6)

2.

NAME ______________________________

DATE ________ CLASS SECTION ________

NAME ________________________________

DATE ________ CLASS SECTION ________

(in thousands)

6. Retained Earnings

7. Treasury Stock (at cost)

8. Property, Plant and Equipment, Net

NAME ________________________

DATE ________ CLASS SECTION ________

1.

2.

3.

Taxes on Income — Current

4.

5.	Payment	P. V. Factor	Discounted Value

6.

WORKSHEETS